Mastering 11+

Multiple Choice
COMPREHENSION
Practice Book 1

ashkraft
EDUCATIONAL

Mastering 11+ © 2014 ashkraft educational

www.mastering11plus.com

This page is intentionally left blank

Mastering 11+
Multiple Choice
COMPREHENSION
Practice Book 1

ISBN: 1910678031
ISBN-13:   978-1910678039

9 781910 678039

Second Edition

References:

The Project Gutenbert Ebooks:
What Katy Did, by Susan Coolidge
Cornelli, by Johanna Spyri
Black Beauty, by Anna Sewell
Jo's Boys, by Louisa May Alcott
American Fairy Tales, by L. Frank Baum

AND

British Library Article by Professor David Stevenson
Letter to my mother during WW I by Rohan James Prakash

DEDICATION

To all the teachers who inspire hope, ignite the imagination and instill love of learning amongst their students

"The roots of education are bitter, but the fruit is sweet."

Aristotle

Table of Contents

Multiple Choice

Comprehension Exercises

EXERCISE 1

Instructions: Read the passage carefully and then answer the questions that follow. Record your answer on the answer sheet by choosing one of the options.

Katy's name was Katy Carr. She lived in the town of Burnet, which wasn't a very big town, but was growing as fast as it knew how. The house she lived in stood on the edge of the town. It was a large square house, white, with green blinds, and had a porch in front, over which roses and clematis made a thick bower. Four tall locust trees shaded the gravel path which led to the front gate. On one side of the house was an orchard; on the other side were wood piles and barns, and an ice-house. Behind was a kitchen garden sloping to the south; and behind that a pasture with a brook in it, and butternut trees, and four cows—two red ones, a yellow one with sharp horns tipped with tin, and a dear little white one named Daisy.

There were six of the Carr children—four girls and two boys. Katy, the oldest, was twelve years old; little Phil, the youngest, was four, and the rest fitted in between.

Dr. Carr, their Papa, was a dear, kind, busy man, who was away from home all day, and sometimes all night, too, taking care of sick people. The children hadn't any Mamma. She had died when Phil was a baby, four years before my story began. Katy could remember her pretty well; to the rest she was but a sad, sweet name, spoken on Sunday, and at prayer-times, or when Papa was especially gentle and solemn.

In place of this Mamma, whom they recollected so dimly, there was Aunt Izzie, Papa's sister, who came to take care of them when Mamma went away on that long journey, from which, for so many months, the little ones kept hoping she might return. Aunt Izzie was a small woman, sharp-faced and thin, rather old-looking, and very neat and particular about everything. She meant to be kind to the children, but they puzzled her much, because they were not a bit like herself when she was a child. Aunt Izzie had been a gentle, tidy little thing, who loved to sit as Curly Locks did, sewing long seams in the parlor, and to have her head patted by older people, and be told that she was a good girl; whereas Katy tore her dress every day, hated sewing, and didn't care a button about being called "good," while Clover and Elsie shied off like restless ponies when any one tried to pat their heads. It was very perplexing to Aunt Izzie, and she found it hard to quite forgive the children for being so "unaccountable," and so little like the good boys and girls in Sunday-school memoirs, who were the young people she liked best, and understood most about.

Then Dr. Carr was another person who worried her. He wished to have the children hardy and bold, and encouraged climbing and rough plays, in spite of the bumps and ragged clothes which resulted. In fact, there was just one half-hour of the day when Aunt Izzie was really satisfied about her charges, and that was the half-hour before breakfast, when she had made a law that they were all to sit in their little chairs and learn the Bible verse for the day. At this time she looked at them with pleased eyes, they were all so spick and span, with such nicely-brushed jackets and such neatly-combed hair. But the moment the bell rang her comfort was over. From that time on, they were what she called "not fit to be seen." The neighbors pitied her very much. They used to count the sixty stiff white pantalette legs hung out to dry every Monday morning, and say to each other what a sight of washing those children made, and what a chore it must be for poor Miss Carr to keep them so nice. But poor Miss Carr didn't think them at all nice; that was the worst of it.

QUESTIONS

1 What was the colour of Katy's house?

A. Rose

B. Yellow

C. White

D. Green

2 Why was Papa away from home most of time?

A. Because the children had no Mamma

B. Because he was sick and hospitalised

C. Because he was busy looking after the sick

D. Because there was Aunt Izzie to look after the children

3 | **How many siblings did Katy have?**

A. Six

B. Five

C. Four

D. Two

4 | **Why did the children puzzle Aunt Izzie?**

A. Because the children read the bible and were always tidy

B. Because the children were so kind for their age

C. Because the children reminded her of herself when she was a child

D. Because the children were not like her when she was a child

5 | **Why did Aunt Izzie like the half-hour before the breakfast?**

A. Children were out playing at that time

B. Children looked nice and tidy as she wanted them to

C. Children cooked breakfast for her

D. Papa looked after the children during that half-hour

6 | **Papa was another person who worried Aunt Izzie. Why?**

A. He was always away from home

B. He was busy looking after the sick people

C. He encouraged children play rough

D. He was always late to the breakfast table

7 | **Why did the neighbours pity Aunt Izzie?**

A. Because they thought she worked really hard to keep the children clean

B. Because the children did not love her

C. Because she was always left alone

D. Because she looked too old for her age

8 | **Who was Daisy?**

A. The youngest of the children

B. The eldest of the children

C. One of the neighbours who pitied Aunt Izzie

D. One of the four cows

9 | **How old was Phil at the time of the story?**

A. Twelve

B. Four

C. Somewhere between four and twelve

D. A baby

10 | **What is the meaning of the word "perplexing"?**

A. Puzzling

B. Naive

C. Flexible

D. Meek

Mastering 11+ / COMPREHENSION / Practice Book ONE

ANSWER SHEET

	A	B	C	D			A	B	C	D
1	A	B	C	D		**6**	A	B	C	D
2	A	B	C	D		**7**	A	B	C	D
3	A	B	C	D		**8**	A	B	C	D
4	A	B	C	D		**9**	A	B	C	D
5	A	B	C	D		**10**	A	B	C	D

EXERCISE 2

Instructions: Read the passage carefully and then answer the questions that follow. Record your answer on the answer sheet by choosing one of the options.

Tackleton the Toy merchant, pretty generally known as Gruff and Tackleton—for that was the firm, though Gruff had been bought out long ago; only leaving his name, and, as some said, his nature, according to its Dictionary meaning, in the business—Tackleton the Toy merchant was a man whose vocation had been quite misunderstood by his Parents and Guardians. If they had made him a Money Lender, or a sharp Attorney, or a Sheriff's Officer, or a Broker, he might have sown his discontented oats in his youth, and, after having had the full run of himself in ill-natured transactions, might have turned out amiable, at last, for the sake of a little freshness and novelty. But, cramped and chafing in the peaceable pursuit of toy making, he was a domestic Ogre, who had been living on children all his life, and was their implacable enemy. He despised all toys; wouldn't have bought one for the world; delighted, in his malice, to insinuate grim expressions into the faces of brown-paper farmers who drove pigs to market, bellmen who advertised lost lawyers' consciences, movable old ladies who darned stockings or carved pies; and other like samples of his stock-in-trade. In appalling masks; hideous, hairy, red-eyed Jacks in Boxes; Vampire Kites; demoniacal Tumblers who wouldn't lie down, and were perpetually flying forward, to stare infants out of countenance; his soul perfectly revelled. They were his only relief, and safety-valve. He was great in such inventions. Anything suggestive of a Pony nightmare was delicious to him. He had even lost money (and he took to that toy very kindly) by getting up Goblin slides for magic lanterns, whereon the Powers of Darkness were depicted as a sort of supernatural shell-fish, with human faces. In intensifying the portraiture of Giants, he had sunk quite a little capital; and, though no painter himself, he could indicate, for the instruction of his artists, with a piece of chalk, a certain furtive leer for the countenances of those monsters, which was safe to destroy the peace of mind of any young gentleman between the ages of six and eleven, for the whole Christmas or Midsummer Vacation.

What he was in toys, he was (as most men are) in other things. You may easily suppose, therefore, that within the great green cape, which reached down to the calves of his legs, there was buttoned up to the chin an uncommonly pleasant fellow; and that he was about as choice a spirit, and as agreeable a companion, as ever stood in a pair of bull-headed-looking boots with mahogany-coloured tops.

Still, Tackleton, the toy merchant, was going to be married. In spite of all this, he was going to be married. And to a young wife too, a beautiful young wife.

He didn't look much like a Bridegroom, as he stood in the Carrier's kitchen, with a twist in his dry face, and a screw in his body, and his hat jerked over the bridge of his nose, and his hands tucked down into the bottoms of his pockets, and his whole sarcastic, ill-conditioned self-peering out of one little corner of one little eye, like the concentrated essence of any number of ravens. But a Bridegroom he designed to be.

"In three days' time. Next Thursday. The last day of the first month in the year. That's my wedding-day," said Tackleton.

Did I mention that he had always one eye wide open, and one eye nearly shut; and that the one eye nearly shut was always the expressive eye? I don't think I did.

"That's my wedding-day!" said Tackleton, rattling his money.

"Why, it's our wedding-day too," exclaimed the Carrier.

QUESTIONS

1 What is the name of the toy company mentioned in this story?

    A. Tackleton

    B. Carrier

    C. Tackleton & Carrier

    D. Tackleton & Gruff

2 Who owns the toy company?

    A. Gruff

    B. Tackleton & Gruff

    C. Tackleton

    D. Carrier

3   **What does the word Gruff mean?**

    A. Grumpy

    B. Outgoing

    C. Sociable

    D. Friendly

4   **What was Tackleton's profession?**

    A. Broker

    B. Attorney

    C. Toy maker

    D. Sherriff

5   **What kind of inventions thrilled Tackleton?**

    A. Hideous toys that would scare children

    B. Hairy toys

    C. Kites

    D. Creative drawing with chalk

6   **What aspect of Teckleton's toys made the young boys lose their peace of mind?**

    A. The gory nature of his toys

    B. Scarcity of the toys

    C. The audacity of the design

    D. The high cost of the toys

7 | **What was the colour of Teckleton's cloak?**

    A. Mahogany

    B. Red

    (C.) Green

    D. Grey

8 | **Where is Teckleton when he is speaking to Carrier?**

    A. In the toy factory

    B. In the wedding hall

    (C.) Carrier's kitchen

    D. Not clear from the passage

9 | **Who else had their wedding day on the same day?**

    (A.) Carrier

    B. Gruff

    C. Toy Merchant

    D. Sheriff's officer

10 | **Which of the following best describes Teckleton?**

    A. Pleasant

    B. Congenial

    C. Affable

    (D.) Abominable

	A	B	C	D			A	B	C	D
1	▭	▭	▭	▭		6	▭	▭	▭	▭
2	▭	▭	▭	▭		7	▭	▭	▭	▭
3	▭	▭	▭	▭		8	▭	▭	▭	▭
4	▭	▭	▭	▭		9	▭	▭	▭	▭
5	▭	▭	▭	▭		10	▭	▭	▭	▭

EXERCISE 3

Instructions: Read the passage carefully and then answer the questions that follow. Record your answer on the answer sheet by choosing one of the options.

World War I

Written by Professor David Stevenson

In July-August 1914 an international crisis culminated in the outbreak of the First World War. The crisis had three phases. In the first, one of the six European Great Powers, Austria-Hungary, launched a war against Serbia. In the second, this war escalated into a Continent-wide conflict involving Germany, Russia, and France. In the third, the conflict spread into Western Europe as Germany invaded Luxemburg and Belgium, and Britain intervened. The sixth Great Power, Italy, remained neutral.

It began with the assassinations on 28 June of the Archduke Franz Ferdinand and his wife, Sophie, at Sarajevo by Gavrilo Princip. Franz Ferdinand was heir to the Austro-Hungarian throne. He fell victim to what would now be called state-sponsored terrorism. Princip was an ethnic Serb from Bosnia, which Austria-Hungary had annexed in 1908. He belonged to a revolutionary nationalist group that wanted to liberate the South Slav peoples (Serbs, Croats, and Slovenes) from foreign rule and unite them in a new state of Yugoslavia. The conspirators had received their weapons from Serbian military intelligence and been trained in Belgrade, although the Serbian civilian government had not been involved. It was therefore unsurprising that Austria-Hungary made drastic demands on Serbia in an ultimatum delivered on 23 July. But the Austro-Hungarian leaders wanted to use the assassinations to provoke a war, and to a British radical such as David Lloyd George their conduct amounted to bullying. When Serbia failed to accept all of the demands, Austria-Hungary declared war on 28 July.

Austria-Hungary's leaders ruled a multi-national empire. They felt that Serbian-backed separatism threatened its survival. Already by 1913 they had decided that only force could solve the problem. But they knew a war against Serbia was almost certain to escalate, and before sending the ultimatum they consulted their ally, Germany, whose leaders urged Austria-Hungary to use force and promised backing if Russia intervened. The German leaders were readier to risk war because they believed the current military balance favoured them but would soon deteriorate. But if Germany threw down a challenge, Russia was quick to respond. Once Austria-Hungary sent the ultimatum Russia began military preparations, and after war was declared on Serbia, Russia ordered 'general mobilisation', placing its forces on a war footing. Russia's leaders were willing to accept a European conflict rather than abandon Serbia. They had recently strengthened their army, and they correctly expected France to support them.

Germany and France had been at odds since the Franco-Prussian War of 1870-71, after which Germany had annexed the French provinces of Alsace-Lorraine. The French remembered the loss, although they would not have started a war over it. Germany's strategy for a war against France and Russia envisaged first defeating France quickly, outflanking France's border fortresses by invading via Luxemburg and Belgium. Once Russia mobilized (which the Germans feared would undermine their war plan) the Germans declared war on both Russia and France and demanded that Belgium allow them to cross its territory. Britain, Germany, and France had all committed themselves to respect Belgian independence by the 1839 Treaty of London, and the issue swung the doubters in the British Cabinet. As Germany failed to comply with a demand to respect Belgium, on 4 August Britain declared war.

QUESTIONS

1 **Which one of the six Great Powers of Europe did not take part in the first world war?**

    A. Italy

    B. Germany

    C. France

    D. Belgium

2 **What started the war initially?**

    A. Germany demanding Hungary let them pass through their borders

    B. Austria-Hungary declaring war on Serbia

    C. Germany declaring the war on France and Russia

    D. France staging a war on Germany to take back the occupied provinces

| 3 | **Which country did Austria-Hungary consult before staging the war against Serbia?** |

A. Russia

B. Britain

C. Germany

D. France

| 4 | **Who did Russia expect to support them in case of a war?** |

A. Austria-Hungary

B. Britain

C. Germany

D. France

| 5 | **When did the Franco-Prussian war take place?** |

A. 1914

B. 1913

C. 1870

D. 1839

| 6 | **Which French provinces were occupied by Germans since Franco-Prussian war?** |

A. Alsace-Lorraine

B. Normandy

C. Burgundy

D. Champagne

7 | Who were Germans planning to defeat first in case of a war?

A. Russia

B. France

C. Austria-Hungary

D. Britain

8 | What would have undermined the German's war plan?

A. Britain supporting France

B. Russia going against them

C. Luxembourg not allowing them to pass through their borders

D. France fighting back

9 | Which country did Germans demand that they should be allowed to cross through their territory?

A. Luxembourg

B. Hungary

C. Belgium

D. France

10 | Why did Britain join the war?

A. Because Germans failed to respect Belgium's independence

B. Because France asked for help

C. Because Austria-Hungary declared war on Serbia

D. Because Russia asked for help

1	A ☐	B ☐	C ☐	D ☐		6	A ☐	B ☐	C ☐	D ☐
2	A ☐	B ☐	C ☐	D ☐		7	A ☐	B ☐	C ☐	D ☐
3	A ☐	B ☐	C ☐	D ☐		8	A ☐	B ☐	C ☐	D ☐
4	A ☐	B ☐	C ☐	D ☐		9	A ☐	B ☐	C ☐	D ☐
5	A ☐	B ☐	C ☐	D ☐		10	A ☐	B ☐	C ☐	D ☐

Instructions: Read the passage carefully and then answer the questions that follow. Record your answer on the answer sheet by choosing one of the options.

One bright morning in May, a portly gentleman, leaning heavily on a gold-headed cane, was walking up the narrow city street. The houses here were so high that the upper windows could scarcely be seen from below. A steep rise in the street caused the gentleman to stop from time to time to get his breath. Scrutinizing the house numbers, he said to himself several times: "Not yet, not yet." Then, climbing up still higher, he at last reached a house beside whose open door six bells were hanging.

The gentleman now began to study the names under the bells, meanwhile gravely shaking his head, for he did not seem to find the name he was seeking.

"Oh dear, at last! and the highest one up, too," he sighed, while he entered the house. Now the real climbing began. At first the steps, though rather high, were white and neat. But after a while they became dark and narrow, and in the end the way led over worn, uneven steps to a narrow door. The only standing room was on the last small step.

"Is this a cage?" said the climber to himself, breathing hard and holding fast to the railing. The thin and creaking steps seemed to him extremely unsafe. After he had pulled the bell-rope, the door opened, and a lady dressed in black stood before him.

"Oh, is it you, kind guardian?" she exclaimed with astonishment. "I am so sorry that you had to come up these winding steps," she added, for she noticed that the stout gentleman had to wipe his face after the great exertion. "I should have been very glad to go down to you, if you had let me know that you were here." The lady meanwhile had led the gentleman into the room and asked him to seat himself.

"As your guardian I simply had to come once to see you," he declared, seating himself on an old sofa and still leaning with both hands on the golden knob of his cane. "I have to tell you, my dear Mrs. Halm, that I am sorry you moved to town. You should have followed my advice and lived in a small house in the country. It would have been so much more practical for you than to live in this garret lodging where you have no conveniences whatever. I am quite sure that the country air would have been much better for both you and the children."

"I could not think about conveniences for myself, when my husband died, and I had to leave the parsonage, Mr. Schaller," replied the lady, with a faint smile. "The country air would naturally have been much better for my children, especially for my older boy.

But he had to come to town on account of school, and I could not possibly have sent him away from me, delicate as he is. Besides——"

"There are boarding places in town where such boys are well taken care of," the visitor interrupted. "What other reasons did you have?"

"My girls, too, are old enough to learn something which they can make use of later on," continued the lady. "You know that this is necessary and that it is very hard to get such opportunities in the country. I hope I have persuaded you that coming to town with the children was not a foolish undertaking. I am extremely glad that you have given me an opportunity to explain why I did not follow your advice."

"What are your daughters going to learn?" the gentleman asked abruptly.

"Nika, the elder, paints quite well," replied the lady, "and Agnes has a decided talent for music. If both girls are earnest in their studies, they hope later on to be able to teach; indeed, they are very anxious to do so."

"These arts do not bring good returns, even after years and years of study," said the gentleman. "It would be much more sensible for the sisters to busy themselves with dressmaking. They could quickly begin a business in which they might help each other and make some money. This would really help both you and your son a great deal. If your boy is going to study, it will be a long time before he can be independent."

The parson's widow looked sadly in front of her without saying a word.

1 **What was the name of portly gentleman?**

    A. Mr. Parson

    B. Mr. Schaller

    C. Mr. Halm

    D. Not mentioned in the passage

2 **What made the gentleman stop to get his breath every now and then?**

    A. His old age

    B. The steep rise in the street

    C. The cane he was carrying was heavy

    D. He has been looking for the house for too long

3 **Why did the gentleman call the house a "cage"?**

    A. It was a small place with dark, worn and narrow stairs leading to it

    B. It had no windows

    C. It was in a narrow town

    D. It was the top most house

4 **Why did the gentleman think country living is best for Mrs. Halm?**

    A. So she could send her son to a boarding school

    B. It was more practical and the fresh air would benefit her and her children

    C. He despised living in a town

    D. The daughters could find jobs easily in a country

5 What do you think is the meaning of "garret lodging" in reference the lady's house?

   A. Living in a penthouse

   B. Living in an attic

   C. A bird's nest

   D. A lion's den

6 What was Mrs. Halm's justification for moving to town?

   A. The death of her husband

   B. The convenience of living in a town

   C. Her son's schooling

   D. The fresh air

7 What was Mrs. Halm was thankful to the gentleman for?

   A. The opportunity to explain why she did not follow his advice

   B. The opportunity to move back to the country

   C. The opportunity to send her son to the boarding school

   D. The help in finding her daughters a job

8 What profession did the lady think her daughters will go into?

   A. Musicians

   B. Artists

   C. Teaching

   D. Medicine

9   **How many children did Mrs. Halm have?**

A.   Two

B.   Three

C.   One

D.   Four

10   **Who was the gentleman?**

A.   Guardian to Mrs. Halm and her children

B.   A family friend of Mrs. Halm

C.   A well wisher

D.   A passer-by

ANSWER SHEET

1	A	B	C	D		6	A	B	C	D
2	A	B	C	D		7	A	B	C	D
3	A	B	C	D		8	A	B	C	D
4	A	B	C	D		9	A	B	C	D
5	A	B	C	D		10	A	B	C	D

EXERCISE 5

Instructions: Read the passage carefully and then answer the questions that follow. Record your answer on the answer sheet by choosing one of the options.

I was now beginning to grow handsome; my coat had grown fine and soft, and was bright black. I had one white foot and a pretty white star on my forehead. I was thought very handsome; my master would not sell me till I was four years old; he said lads ought not to work like men, and colts ought not to work like horses till they were quite grown up.

When I was four years old Squire Gordon came to look at me. He examined my eyes, my mouth, and my legs; he felt them all down; and then I had to walk and trot and gallop before him. He seemed to like me, and said, "When he has been well broken in he will do very well." My master said he would break me in himself, as he should not like me to be frightened or hurt, and he lost no time about it, for the next day he began.

Every one may not know what breaking in is, therefore I will describe it. It means to teach a horse to wear a saddle and bridle, and to carry on his back a man, woman or child; to go just the way they wish, and to go quietly. Besides this he has to learn to wear a collar, a crupper, and a breeching, and to stand still while they are put on; then to have a cart or a chaise fixed behind, so that he cannot walk or trot without dragging it after him; and he must go fast or slow, just as his driver wishes. He must never start at what he sees, nor speak to other horses, nor bite, nor kick, nor have any will of his own; but always do his master's will, even though he may be very tired or hungry; but the worst of all is, when his harness is once on, he may neither jump for joy nor lie down for weariness. So you see this breaking in is a great thing.

I had of course long been used to a halter and a headstall, and to be led about in the fields and lanes quietly, but now I was to have a bit and bridle; my master gave me some oats as usual, and after a good deal of coaxing he got the bit into my mouth, and the bridle fixed, but it was a nasty thing! Those who have never had a bit in their mouths cannot think how bad it feels; a great piece of cold hard steel as thick as a man's finger to be pushed into one's mouth, between one's teeth, and over one's tongue, with the ends coming out at the corner of your mouth, and held fast there by straps over your head, under your throat, round your nose, and under your chin; so that no way in the world can you get rid of the nasty hard thing; it is very bad! yes, very bad! at least I thought so; but I knew my mother always wore one when she went out, and all horses did when they were grown up; and so, what with the nice oats, and what with my master's pats, kind words, and gentle ways, I got to wear my bit and bridle.

Next came the saddle, but that was not half so bad; my master put it on my back very gently, while old Daniel held my head; he then made the girths fast under my body, patting and talking to me all the time; then I had a few oats, then a little leading about; and this he did every day till I began to look for the oats and the saddle. At length, one morning, my master got on my back and rode me round the meadow on the soft grass. It certainly did feel queer; but I must say I felt rather proud to carry my master, and as he continued to ride me a little every day I soon became accustomed to it.

The next unpleasant business was putting on the iron shoes; that too was very hard at first. My master went with me to the smith's forge, to see that I was not hurt or got any fright. The blacksmith took my feet in his hand, one after the other, and cut away some of the hoof. It did not pain me, so I stood still on three legs till he had done them all. Then he took a piece of iron the shape of my foot, and clapped it on, and drove some nails through the shoe quite into my hoof, so that the shoe was firmly on. My feet felt very stiff and heavy, but in time I got used to it.

And now having got so far, my master went on to break me to harness; there were more new things to wear. First, a stiff heavy collar just on my neck, and a bridle with great side-pieces against my eyes called blinkers, and blinkers indeed they were, for I could not see on either side, but only straight in front of me; next, there was a small saddle with a nasty stiff strap that went right under my tail; that was the crupper. I hated the crupper; to have my long tail doubled up and poked through that strap was almost as bad as the bit. I never felt more like kicking, but of course I could not kick such a good master, and so in time I got used to everything, and could do my work as well as my mother.

I must not forget to mention one part of my training, which I have always considered a very great advantage. My master sent me for a fortnight to a neighboring farmer's, who had a meadow which was skirted on one side by the railway. Here were some sheep and cows, and I was turned in among them.

1 Who is narrating this story?

A. A horse

B. Squire Gordon

C. The master

D. Daniel

2 What does "breaking" mean?

A. Fixing a heavy collar

B. Teaching a horse how to carry a person

C. Being used for halter and a headstall

D. Feeding oats

3 What is the meaning of the word "coaxing"?

A. Cajoling

B. Forcing

C. Imposing

D. Coercing

4 | **Why do you think the colt was fed oats while putting the saddle on?**

A. To get the colt into a habit of oats and then saddle

B. To get its attention away from the saddle

C. To make sure it wasn't hungry

D. It is not clear from this passage

5 | **When the master rode for the first time the colt felt queer.**
What does queer mean?

A. Scared

B. Painful

C. Heavy

D. Strange

6 | **Who clapped the iron shoes on the colt's feet?**

A. The master

B. Daniel

C. Squire Gordon

D. The blacksmith

7 | **Why did the master go to smith's forge?**

A. To help cut some of the hoof

B. To pay for the iron shoes

C. To make sure the colt was not hurt

D. To help the person clapping the iron shoes

8 What are blinkers used for?

(A.) To make sure a colt can only see straight in front

B. To ensure the horse does not get a fright

C. To help the rider control the speed of the horse

D. To help fix the iron shoe

9 When did the colt feel like kicking out?

A. When they drove some nails through the shoe into the hoof

(B.) When the tail was doubled up and poked through the Crupper

C. When some of the hoof was cut away

D. When the bit was inserted into colt's mouth

10 Where did the master send the colt for a fortnight?

A. To the smith's forge

(B.) The meadow along which ran a railway track

C. To a racing course

D. To the stable

ANSWER SHEET

	A	B	C	D		A	B	C	D
1	A	B	C	D	6	A	B	C	D
2	A	B	C	D	7	A	B	C	D
3	A	B	C	D	8	A	B	C	D
4	A	B	C	D	9	A	B	C	D
5	A	B	C	D	10	A	B	C	D

EXERCISE 6

Instructions: Read the passage carefully and then answer the questions that follow. Record your answer on the answer sheet by choosing one of the options.

When the princess came to the top, she found herself in a little square place, with three doors, two opposite each other, and one opposite the top of the stair. She stood for a moment, without an idea in her little head what to do next. But as she stood, she began to hear a curious humming sound. Could it be the rain? No. It was much more gentle, and even monotonous than the sound of the rain, which now she scarcely heard. The low sweet humming sound went on, sometimes stopping for a little while and then beginning again. It was more like the hum of a very happy bee that had found a rich well of honey in some globular flower, than anything else I can think of at this moment. Where could it come from? She laid her ear first to one of the doors to hearken if it was there—then to another. When she laid her ear against the third door, there could be no doubt where it came from: it must be from something in that room. What could it be? She was rather afraid, but her curiosity was stronger than her fear, and she opened the door very gently and peeped in. What do you think she saw? A very old lady who sat spinning.

Perhaps you will wonder how the princess could tell that the old lady was an old lady, when I inform you that not only was she beautiful, but her skin was smooth and white. I will tell you more. Her hair was combed back from her forehead and face, and hung loose far down and all over her back. That is not much like an old lady—is it? Ah! but it was white almost as snow. And although her face was so smooth, her eyes looked so wise that you could not have helped seeing she must be old. The princess, though she could not have told you why, did think her very old indeed—quite fifty, she said to herself. But she was rather older than that, as you shall hear.

While the princess stared bewildered, with her head just inside the door, the old lady lifted hers, and said, in a sweet, but old and rather shaky voice, which mingled very pleasantly with the continued hum of her wheel: 'Come in, my dear; come in. I am glad to see you.'

That the princess was a real princess you might see now quite plainly; for she didn't hang on to the handle of the door, and stare without moving, as I have known some do who ought to have been princesses but were only rather vulgar little girls. She did as she was told, stepped inside the door at once, and shut it gently behind her.

'Come to me, my dear,' said the old lady.

And again the princess did as she was told. She approached the old lady—rather slowly, I confess—but did not stop until she stood by her side, and looked up in her face with her blue eyes and the two melted stars in them. 'Why, what have you been doing with your eyes, child?' asked the old lady. 'Crying,' answered the princess.

'Why, child?'

'Because I couldn't find my way down again.'

'But you could find your way up.'

'Not at first—not for a long time.'

'But your face is streaked like the back of a zebra. Hadn't you a handkerchief to wipe your eyes with?'

'No.'

'Then why didn't you come to me to wipe them for you?'

'Please, I didn't know you were here. I will next time.'

'There's a good child!' said the old lady.

Then she stopped her wheel, and rose, and, going out of the room, returned with a little silver basin and a soft white towel, with which she washed and wiped the bright little face. And the princess thought her hands were so smooth and nice! When she carried away the basin and towel, the little princess wondered to see how straight and tall she was, for, although she was so old, she didn't stoop a bit. She was dressed in black velvet with thick white heavy-looking lace about it; and on the black dress her hair shone like silver. There was hardly any more furniture in the room than there might have been in that of the poorest old woman who made her bread by her spinning. There was no carpet on the floor—no table anywhere—nothing but the spinning-wheel and the chair beside it. When she came back, she sat down and without a word began her spinning once more, while Irene, who had never seen a spinning-wheel, stood by her side and looked on. When the old lady had got her thread fairly going again, she said to the princess, but without looking at her:

'Do you know my name, child?'

'No, I don't know it,' answered the princess.

'My name is Irene.'

'That's my name!' cried the princess.

'I know that. I let you have mine. I haven't got your name. You've got mine.'

| 1 | **Where was the princess when she heard the humming sound?** |

A. In her bedroom

B. In her garden

C. Top of the stairs

D. In her kitchen

| 2 | **What was the source of the humming sound?** |

A. An old lady humming

B. Sound of the rain

C. The buzz of a bee

D. The squeaking sound of the door

| 3 | **What was the old lady behind one of the doors doing?** |

A. Collecting eggs

B. Spinning

C. Cleaning the floor

D. Singing a song

4 What according to the author proves that the little girl was a genuine princess?

A. Her walking in without fear as soon as she was asked to come in

B. Her making sure it was safe to walk into the room with a stranger

C. Her striking up a royal conversation

D. Her enquiring about the old lady's wellbeing

5 How old was the lady according to princess?

A. Too old

B. About fifty

C. More than Fifty

D. Can't tell from this passage

6 Why was the princess crying when she met the old lady?

A. For she could not find her way back down

B. For she could not reach the old lady in time

C. For she did not know where the old lady was

D. She was too far away from her palace

7 What did the old lady use to clean and wipe the face of princess?

A. Water and towel

B. Soap and water

C. Silver basin and soft white towel

D. Water and black velvet

| 8 | What made the princess wonder about when she saw the old woman walk? |

A. How her face was still smooth and white

B. How the old lady did not stoop one bit while walking

C. How her eyes looked wise

D. How the poor old lady made her bread by spinning

| 9 | What was the name of the old lady? |

A. Irene

B. Velvet

C. Nursie

D. Princess Irene

| 10 | What was unusual about the old lady's name? |

A. It was the same as that of the princess

B. She had the name of a man

C. It was the same name as the queen

D. It was the same name as princess' grandmother

9/10

ANSWER SHEET

1	A	B	C	D		6	A	B	C	D
2	A	B	C	D		7	A	B	C	D
3	A	B	C	D		8	A	B	C	D
4	A	B	C	D		9	A	B	C	D
5	A	B	C	D		10	A	B	C	D

Mastering 11+ / COMPREHENSION / Practice Book ONE

EXERCISE 7

Instructions: Read the passage carefully and then answer the questions that follow. Record your answer on the answer sheet by choosing one of the options.

When princess Irene woke the next morning, the first thing she heard was the rain still falling. Indeed, this day was so like the last that it would have been difficult to tell where was the use of it. The first thing she thought of, however, was not the rain, but the lady in the tower; and the first question that occupied her thoughts was whether she should not ask the nurse to fulfil her promise this very morning, and go with her to find her grandmother as soon as she had had her breakfast. But she came to the conclusion that perhaps the lady would not be pleased if she took anyone to see her without first asking leave; especially as it was pretty evident, seeing she lived on pigeons' eggs, and cooked them herself, that she did not want the household to know she was there. So the princess resolved to take the first opportunity of running up alone and asking whether she might bring her nurse. She believed the fact that she could not otherwise convince her she was telling the truth would have much weight with her grandmother.

The princess and her nurse were the best of friends all dressing-time, and the princess in consequence ate an enormous little breakfast.

'I wonder, Lootie'—that was her pet name for her nurse—'what pigeons' eggs taste like?' she said, as she was eating her egg—not quite a common one, for they always picked out the pinky ones for her.

'We'll get you a pigeon's egg, and you shall judge for yourself,' said the nurse.

'Oh, no, no!' returned Irene, suddenly reflecting they might disturb the old lady in getting it, and that even if they did not, she would have one less in consequence.

'What a strange creature you are,' said the nurse—'first to want a thing and then to refuse it!'

But she did not say it crossly, and the princess never minded any remarks that were not unfriendly.

'Well, you see, Lootie, there are reasons,' she returned, and said no more, for she did not want to bring up the subject of their former strife, lest her nurse should offer to go before she had had her grandmother's permission to bring her. Of course she could refuse to take her, but then she would believe her less than ever.

Now the nurse, as she said herself afterwards, could not be every moment in the room; and as never before yesterday had the princess given her the smallest reason for anxiety, it had not yet come into her head to watch her more closely. So she soon gave her a chance, and, the very first that offered, Irene was off and up the stairs again.

This day's adventure, however, did not turn out like yesterday's, although it began like it; and indeed to-day is very seldom like yesterday, if people would note the differences—even when it rains. The princess ran through passage after passage, and could not find the stair of the tower. My own suspicion is that she had not gone up high enough, and was searching on the second instead of the third floor. When she turned to go back, she failed equally in her search after the stair. She was lost once more.

Something made it even worse to bear this time, and it was no wonder that she cried again. Suddenly it occurred to her that it was after having cried before that she had found her grandmother's stair. She got up at once, wiped her eyes, and started upon a fresh quest.

This time, although she did not find what she hoped, she found what was next best: she did not come on a stair that went up, but she came upon one that went down. It was evidently not the stair she had come up, yet it was a good deal better than none; so down she went, and was singing merrily before she reached the bottom. There, to her surprise, she found herself in the kitchen. Although she was not allowed to go there alone, her nurse had often taken her, and she was a great favourite with the servants. So there was a general rush at her the moment she appeared, for every one wanted to have her; and the report of where she was soon reached the nurse's ears. She came at once to fetch her; but she never suspected how she had got there, and the princess kept her own counsel.

QUESTIONS

1	What was the first thing the princess thought of when she woke up?

A. Breakfast

B. The promise the nurse had made

C. The rain

D. Lady in the tower

2   **What promise had the nurse made to the princess?**

     A. To serve her a big breakfast

     B. To take her to the kitchen

     C. To find her grandmother

     D. To take her to the tower

3   **Who did the princess think will be unhappy, if she took someone to see her, without her prior permission?**

     A. The lady in tower

     B. Nurse

     C. The Queen

     D. Irene

4   **What according princess did the lady in tower live on?**

     A. Breakfast

     B. Eggs

     C. Fruits

     D. Pigeon's eggs

5   **What made the princess eat an enormous little breakfast?**

     A. The friendliness between her and the nurse

     B. Her excitement about the pigeon's eggs

     C. The delicious taste

     D. Princess wanted to please the nurse

6 | **What was the pet name for the nurse?**

A. Nursie

B. Irene

C. Lootie

D. The bear

7 | **Why did the nurse say the princess is a strange "creature"?**

A. Because she changed her mind on finding pigeon's eggs

B. Because she wanted to find a grandmother that didn't exist

C. Because she ate an enormous little breakfast

D. Because she was unusually friendly with her

8 | **Who was the lady in the tower?**

A. An imaginary friend of the princess

B. Princess's great-great-grandmother

C. The Queen

D. A lady whom the princess called "Lootie"

9 | **Why could the princess not find the stairs leading up to the tower?**

A. Because they never existed

B. Because she was searching on the wrong floor

C. Because she was in the kitchen

D. Because it wasn't raining

10   Where did the stairs going down take the princess?

     A.   To the tower

     B.   To the third floor

     C.   To the kitchen

     D.   To the garden

ANSWER SHEET

	A	B	C	D			A	B	C	D
1	▭	▭	▭	▭		6	▭	▭	▭	▭
2	▭	▭	▭	▭		7	▭	▭	▭	▭
3	▭	▭	▭	▭		8	▭	▭	▭	▭
4	▭	▭	▭	▭		9	▭	▭	▭	▭
5	▭	▭	▭	▭		10	▭	▭	▭	▭

Instructions: Read this letter written by a young soldier during World War 1 carefully and then answer the questions that follow. Record your answer on the answer sheet by choosing one of the options. The young man who wrote this letter left his mother to join the war against the Kaiser (which means the leader in Germany), against her wish. He was only fifteen and lied about his age to join the army as he was keen.

17/10/1914

Dear Ma,

I am sorry to leave you like this but it is every man's duty to fight for the future. Also, I knew that Pa would be proud of me and I want a crack at the Kaiser.

I made it through to the army and they say I am a good shot. Still, I am toyed around and left out much of the time. They are yet to kit me as there is lack of uniforms here. Boss says I'm a good notch but armed only with a pistol and dagger. We are cramped by a dozen men in each bell tent. Food, horrible and the drill is harsh.

Lads are great though and can warm even the coldest of the hearts. Their company makes all the shortcomings appear trivial. I enjoy being around them.

When I set off on the ship, filled to the brim, I felt a twinge of guilt. So I snatched a quill and wrote to you, owing you an apology. Just as am about to finish this letter, I could see the French coastline brushing against the murky sea and the lads singing carols to their heart's content. It is warming my soul.

By the time this letter reaches you, I will be on a jam-packed train with a few humbugs to savour.

See you soon.

Fondest Love,

Samuel

17/10/1914
France

1   What does "Kaiser" mean?

    A.   A war

    B.   A soldier

    C.   The enemy

    D.   Leader in Germany

2   What is the young soldier apologising to his mother for?

    A.   For being naughty

    B.   For eating humbugs

    C.   Joining the army and leaving without her permission

    D.   Going out on a camping trip with his friends

3   How old was the soldier at the time of writing this letter?

    A.   Fifteen

    B.   Sixteen

    C.   Twenty One

    D.   Difficult to tell from the letter

4   When was this letter written?

    A.   During World War II

    B.   1914, World War I

    C.   1944

    D.   1953

5 What is every man's duty according to the young soldier?

    A. Fight against the Kaiser

    B. Making one's father proud

    C. Fight for the future

    D. Joining the army

6 Why is the soldier yet to be kitted?

    A. There is a concern that he could be too young to join the army

    B. Because his mother has not approved him joining the army

    C. There is a shortage of kits

    D. He is yet to be fully trained

7 Which of the following best describes the conditions in the army camp?

    A. Punitive

    B. Lenient

    C. Merciful

    D. Indulgent

8 What made the soldier feel guilty as he set off on the ship carrying soldiers?

    A. Bad companions

    B. Not telling his mother about him joining the army

    C. Not making his father proud of him

    D. Circumstances that can only be described as twinge

9   What according to the soldier could warm even the coldest of the hearts?

    A.   The food being served at the camp

    B.   The soldiers he is accompanying

    C.   Seeing the French coastline

    D.   Writing to one's mother

10   Where was the soldier just as he was finishing writing this letter?

    A.   On the ship, about to set off

    B.   French coastline

    C.   In France

    D.   In an army camp

ANSWER SHEET

1	A	B	C	D		6	A	B	C	D
2	A	B	C	D		7	A	B	C	D
3	A	B	C	D		8	A	B	C	D
4	A	B	C	D		9	A	B	C	D
5	A	B	C	D		10	A	B	C	D

EXERCISE 9

Instructions: Read the passage carefully and then answer the questions that follow. Record your answer on the answer sheet by choosing one of the options.

The boy who saved Princess Irene and her nurse from the goblins was dressed in a miner's dress, with a curious cap on his head. He was a very nice-looking boy, with eyes as dark as the mines in which he worked and as sparkling as the crystals in their rocks. He was about twelve years old. His face was almost too pale for beauty, which came of his being so little in the open air and the sunlight—for even vegetables grown in the dark are white; but he looked happy, merry indeed—perhaps at the thought of having routed the goblins; and his bearing as he stood before them had nothing clownish or rude about it.

'I saw them,' he went on, 'as I came up; and I'm very glad I did. I knew they were after somebody, but I couldn't see who it was. They won't touch you so long as I'm with you.'

'Why, who are you?' asked the nurse, offended at the freedom with which he spoke to them.

'I'm Peter's son.'

'Who's Peter?'

'Peter the miner.'

'I don't know him.' 'I'm his son, though.'

'And why should the goblins mind you, pray?'

'Because I don't mind them. I'm used to them.'

'What difference does that make?'

'If you're not afraid of them, they're afraid of you. I'm not afraid of them. That's all. But it's all that's wanted—up here, that is. It's a different thing down there. They won't always mind that song even, down there. And if anyone sings it, they stand grinning at him awfully; and if he gets frightened, and misses a word, or says a wrong one, they— oh! don't they give it him!'

'What do they do to him?' asked Irene, with a trembling voice.

'Don't go frightening the princess,' said the nurse.

'The princess!' repeated the little miner, taking off his curious cap. 'I beg your pardon; but you oughtn't to be out so late. Everybody knows that's against the law.'

'Yes, indeed it is!' said the nurse, beginning to cry again. 'And I shall have to suffer for it.'

'What does that matter?' said the boy. 'It must be your fault. It is the princess who will suffer for it. I hope they didn't hear you call her the princess. If they did, they're sure to know her again: they're awfully sharp.'

'Lootie! Lootie!' cried the princess. 'Take me home.'

'Don't go on like that,' said the nurse to the boy, almost fiercely. 'How could I help it? I lost my way.'

'You shouldn't have been out so late. You wouldn't have lost your way if you hadn't been frightened,' said the boy. 'Come along. I'll soon set you right again. Shall I carry your little Highness?'

'Impertinence!' murmured the nurse, but she did not say it aloud, for she thought if she made him angry he might take his revenge by telling someone belonging to the house, and then it would be sure to come to the king's ears. 'No, thank you,' said Irene. 'I can walk very well, though I can't run so fast as nursie. If you will give me one hand, Lootie will give me another, and then I shall get on famously.'

They soon had her between them, holding a hand of each.

'Now let's run,' said the nurse. 'No, no!' said the little miner. 'That's the worst thing you can do. If you hadn't run before, you would not have lost your way. And if you run now, they will be after you in a moment.'

'I don't want to run,' said Irene.

'You don't think of me,' said the nurse.

'Yes, I do, Lootie. The boy says they won't touch us if we don't run.'

'Yes, but if they know at the house that I've kept you out so late I shall be turned away, and that would break my heart.'

'Turned away, Lootie! Who would turn you away?'

'Your papa, child.'

1   **Who did the boy save the Princess and her nurse from?**

     A.   Goblins

     B.   Miners

     C.   Thieves

     D.   Wolves

2   **How old was the boy?**

     A.   Twelve

     B.   Eleven

     C.   Early Teens

     D.   Eighteen

3   **Why do you think the boy was too pale for beauty?**

     A.   He was rarely in the open air and the sunlight

     B.   He was always in the open air and the sunlight

     C.   He was always in the mines

     D.   He had no one to look after him

4   **Who was the boy?**

     A.   Peter the miner

     B.   Son of Peter, the miner

     C.   One of the goblins

     D.   Lootie

5   **Why were the goblins afraid of the boy?**

     A.   Because he could sing

     B.   Because he was very strong

     C.   Because he could run fast and for long

     D.   Because he was not frightened of the goblins

6   **Why did the princess ask Lootie to take her home?**

     A.   Because it was getting late and dark

     B.   She was scared of the little miner

     C.   She was scared of the goblins

     D.   She was hungry

7   **What made the nurse think the boy was cheekily impolite?**

     A.   Because he asked if he should carry the princess back home

     B.   Because of the way he was dressed

     C.   Because his eyes were dark as the mines

     D.   Because he was singing rude

8   **Why did the little miner suggest the princess and nurse not to run?**

     A.   Because the goblins will be after them if they ran again

     B.   Because they could get lost if they run

     C.   Because the princess couldn't run

     D.   Because the nurse did not want to run

9 | **Why was the nurse persistent that they should run back home?**

   A. She was scared of the goblins and wanted to get back home soon

   B. She was scared of darkness

   C. She was worried that she will lose her job for keeping the princess out for too long

   D. She was worried about palace knowing about the goblins chasing the princess

10 | **What would break nurse's heart?**

   A. The miner boy carrying princess back to the palace

   B. Being turned away from the little princess

   C. Losing her job at the palace

   D. Seeing the goblins again

ANSWER SHEET

	A	B	C	D		A	B	C	D
1	▭	▭	▭	▭	6	▭	▭	▭	▭
2	▭	▭	▭	▭	7	▭	▭	▭	▭
3	▭	▭	▭	▭	8	▭	▭	▭	▭
4	▭	▭	▭	▭	9	▭	▭	▭	▭
5	▭	▭	▭	▭	10	▭	▭	▭	▭

EXERCISE 10

Instructions: Read the passage carefully and then answer the questions that follow. Record your answer on the answer sheet by choosing one of the options.

The March family had enjoyed a great many surprises in the course of their varied career, but the greatest of all was when the Ugly Duckling turned out to be, not a swan, but a golden goose, whose literary eggs found such an unexpected market that in ten years Jo's wildest and most cherished dream actually came true. How or why it happened she never clearly understood, but all of a sudden she found herself famous in a small way, and, better still, with a snug little fortune in her pocket to clear away the obstacles of the present and assure the future of her boys.

It began during a bad year when everything went wrong at Plumfield; times were hard, the school dwindled, Jo overworked herself and had a long illness; Laurie and Amy were abroad, and the Bhaers too proud to ask help even of those as near and dear as this generous pair. Confined to her room, Jo got desperate over the state of affairs, till she fell back upon the long-disused pen as the only thing she could do to help fill up the gaps in the income. A book for girls being wanted by a certain publisher, she hastily scribbled a little story describing a few scenes and adventures in the lives of herself and sisters, though boys were more in her line, and with very slight hopes of success sent it out to seek its fortune.

Things always went by contraries with Jo. Her first book, laboured over for years, and launched full of the high hopes and ambitious dreams of youth, foundered on its voyage, though the wreck continued to float long afterward, to the profit of the publisher at least. The hastily written story, sent away with no thought beyond the few dollars it might bring, sailed with a fair wind and a wise pilot at the helm into public favour, and came home heavily laden with an unexpected cargo of gold and glory.

A more astonished woman probably never existed than Josephine Bhaer when her little ship came into port with flags flying, cannon that had been silent before now booming gaily, and, better than all, many kind faces rejoicing with her, many friendly hands grasping hers with cordial congratulations. After that it was plain sailing, and she merely had to load her ships and send them off on prosperous trips, to bring home stores of comfort for all she loved and laboured for.

The fame she never did quite accept; for it takes very little fire to make a great deal of smoke nowadays, and notoriety is not real glory. The fortune she could not doubt, and gratefully received; though it was not half so large a one as a generous world reported it to be. The tide having turned continued to rise, and floated the family comfortably into a snug harbour where the older members could rest secure from storms, and whence the younger ones could launch their boats for the voyage of life.

All manner of happiness, peace, and plenty came in those years to bless the patient waiters, hopeful workers, and devout believers in the wisdom and justice of Him who sends disappointment, poverty, and sorrow to try the love of human hearts and make success the sweeter when it comes. The world saw the prosperity, and kind souls rejoiced over the improved fortunes of the family; but the success Jo valued most, the happiness that nothing could change or take away, few knew much about.

It was the power of making her mother's last years happy and serene; to see the burden of care laid down for ever, the weary hands at rest, the dear face untroubled by any anxiety, and the tender heart free to pour itself out in the wise charity which was its delight. As a girl, Jo's favourite plan had been a room where Marmee could sit in peace and enjoy herself after her hard, heroic life. Now the dream had become a happy fact, and Marmee sat in her pleasant chamber with every comfort and luxury about her, loving daughters to wait on her as infirmities increased, a faithful mate to lean upon, and grand-children to brighten the twilight of life with their dutiful affection. A very precious time to all, for she rejoiced as only mothers can in the good fortunes of their children. She had lived to reap the harvest she sowed; had seen prayers answered, hopes blossom, good gifts bear fruit, peace and prosperity bless the home she had made; and then, like some brave, patient angel, whose work was done, turned her face heavenward, glad to rest.

QUESTIONS

1 **Which word best describes the nature of the March family's career?**

A. Diverse

B. Limited

C. Homogenous

D. Harmonised

2 | **What do you think is "Ugly Duckling"?**

A. A little duck considered not good looking

B. A poem

C. Pet name for Jo

D. Name of Jo's book

3 | **What were the two things that happened to Jo as a result of "Ugly Duckling"?**

A. Fame and Fortune

B. Fame and Obscurity

C. Vagueness and Richness

D. Peace and Joy

4 | **Why did Jo start to write again?**

A. To find something to do during her loneliness, while she was ill

B. A publisher desperately wanted her to write

C. Family's financial difficulties and the hope of making a few dollars

D. The pen that her mother gifted her

5 | **What was Jo's book about?**

A. About the little adventures in the lives of herself and her brothers

B. About the little adventures in the lives of herself and her sisters

C. About the difficulties her mother went through in her life

D. About her imaginary self

6   **What happened to Jo's first book?**

    A.   It was a big success making her a little fortune

    B.   It was not a big success but made her famous

    C.   It made her and the publisher a fortune

    D.   It sank and was a failure

7   **What is the full name of Jo?**

    A.   Jo Murmea

    B.   Josephine Bhaer

    C.   Joanne Bhaer

    D.   Jo Laurie

8   **How big was Jo's fortune?**

    A.   Big enough to provide an affluent living for the family

    B.   Filthy rich

    C.   Bigger than what she could manage

    D.   As big as widely publicised

9   **Which success did Jo value the most?**

    A.   The fame and wealth

    B.   The peaceful life the family could afford

    C.   The affluent home for the family

    D.   Being able to make her mother's final years happy and serene

10 | **What happened to Jo's mother?**

A. She spent most of her time doing charitable work

B. She could live in peace and with no anxiety

C. She died in peace

D. As big as widely publicised

ANSWER SHEET

	A	B	C	D			A	B	C	D
1	A ▭	B ▭	C ▭	D ▭		**6**	A ▭	B ▭	C ▭	D ▭
2	A ▭	B ▭	C ▭	D ▭		**7**	A ▭	B ▭	C ▭	D ▭
3	A ▭	B ▭	C ▭	D ▭		**8**	A ▭	B ▭	C ▭	D ▭
4	A ▭	B ▭	C ▭	D ▭		**9**	A ▭	B ▭	C ▭	D ▭
5	A ▭	B ▭	C ▭	D ▭		**10**	A ▭	B ▭	C ▭	D ▭

EXERCISE 11

Instructions: Read the passage carefully and then answer the questions that follow. Record your answer on the answer sheet by choosing one of the options.

Mrs Jo often thought that Dan had Indian blood in him, not only because of his love of a wild, wandering life, but his appearance; for as he grew up, this became more striking. At twenty-five he was very tall, with sinewy limbs, a keen, dark face, and the alert look of one whose senses were all alive; rough in manner, full of energy, quick with word and blow, eyes full of the old fire, always watchful as if used to keep guard, and a general air of vigour and freshness very charming to those who knew the dangers and delights of his adventurous life. He was looking his best as he sat talking with 'Mother Bhaer', one strong brown hand in hers, and a world of affection in his voice as he said:

'Forget old friends! How could I forget the only home I ever knew? Why, I was in such a hurry to come and tell my good luck that I didn't stop to fix up, you see; though I knew you'd think I looked more like a wild buffalo than ever,' with a shake of his shaggy black head, a tug at his beard, and a laugh that made the room ring.

'I like it; I always had a fancy for banditti—and you look just like one. Mary, being a newcomer, was frightened at your looks and manners. Josie won't know you, but Ted will recognize his Danny in spite of the big beard and flowing mane. They will all be here soon to welcome you; so before they come tell me more about yourself. Why, Dan, dear! it's nearly two years since you were here! Has it gone well with you?' asked Mrs Jo, who had been listening with maternal interest to his account of life in California, and the unexpected success of a small investment he had made.

'First-rate! I don't care for the money, you know. I only want a trifle to pay my way— rather earn as I go, and not be bothered with the care of a lot. It's the fun of the thing coming to me, and my being able to give away, that I like. No use to lay up; I shan't live to be old and need it,—my sort never do,' said Dan, looking as if his little fortune rather oppressed him.

'But if you marry and settle somewhere, as I hope you will, you must have something to begin with, my son. So be prudent and invest your money; don't give it away, for rainy days come to all of us, and dependence would be very hard for you to bear,' answered Mrs Jo with a sage air, though she liked to see that the money-making fever had not seized her lucky boy yet.

Dan shook his head, and glanced about the room as if he already found it rather confined and longed for all out-of-doors again.

1 **What made Mrs. Jo think Dan had Indian blood in him?**

    A. Because he loved wild, wandering life

    B. Because of his strong limbs

    C. Because of his keen dark face and energy

    D. All of the above

2 **Why did Dan think he looked like a wild buffalo?**

    A. Because he had no time to fix himself as he was in a hurry

    B. Because of his strong limbs and dark face

    C. Because he looked like someone who had Indian blood in him

    D. Because he had a fancy for banditti

3 **Who according Mrs. Jo were arriving shortly to welcome Dan?**

    A. Mary

    B. Josie

    C. Ted

    D. All of the above

4 **What does "banditti" mean?**

    A. Outlaws

    B. Strongly built men

    C. Tall, dark and handsome men

    D. Rich men

5 | **Where has Dan travelled from?**

A. California

B. Calcutta

C. From Mother Bhaer's house

D. Wild wide west

6 | **How long has it been since Dan visited Mrs. Jo's house?**

A. Two years

B. Twenty Five years

C. Twelve Years

D. Twenty Years

7 | **"I only want a trifle to pay my way". What did Dan mean by this?**

A. He did not need too much money for a living

B. He liked a trifle

C. He needed a lot of money to maintain his standard of living

D. He was happy to spend as long as he had money

8 | **What was Dan's attitude towards money?**

A. Earn as much as you can while you are young and save it for future

B. Earn well and spend well to maintain a high standard of living

C. Give away any excess that he did not need without worrying about saving up

D. He was obsessed with wealth

9 **What advice did Mrs. Jo give Dan?**

A. Not to give away all his but instead save for a rainy day

B. Marry and settle somewhere nice

C. Not to be oppressed with money

D. Not to catch the money-making fever

10 **What did Mrs. Jo like about Dan?**

A. Dan doing so well in California

B. Dan giving away all his money to charity

C. Dan spending on a lavish living

D. Dan had not lost his personality to the thirst of money making yet

ANSWER SHEET

	A	B	C	D		A	B	C	D
1	A	B	C	D	**6**	A	B	C	D
2	A	B	C	D	**7**	A	B	C	D
3	A	B	C	D	**8**	A	B	C	D
4	A	B	C	D	**9**	A	B	C	D
5	A	B	C	D	**10**	A	B	C	D

Instructions: Read the passage carefully and then answer the questions that follow. Record your answer on the answer sheet by choosing one of the options.

An accomplished wizard once lived on the top floor of a tenement house and passed his time in thoughtful study and studious thought. What he didn't know about wizardry was hardly worth knowing, for he possessed all the books and recipes of all the wizards who had lived before him; and, moreover, he had invented several wizardments himself.

This admirable person would have been completely happy but for the numerous interruptions to his studies caused by folk who came to consult him about their troubles (in which he was not interested), and by the loud knocks of the iceman, the milkman, the baker's boy, the laundryman and the peanut woman. He never dealt with any of these people; but they rapped at his door every day to see him about this or that or to try to sell him their wares. Just when he was most deeply interested in his books or engaged in watching the bubbling of a cauldron there would come a knock at his door. And after sending the intruder away he always found he had lost his train of thought or ruined his compound.

At length these interruptions aroused his anger, and he decided he must have a dog to keep people away from his door. He didn't know where to find a dog, but in the next room lived a poor glass-blower with whom he had a slight acquaintance; so he went into the man's apartment and asked:

"Where can I find a dog?"

"What sort of a dog?" inquired the glass-blower.

"A good dog. One that will bark at people and drive them away. One that will be no trouble to keep and won't expect to be fed. One that has no fleas and is neat in his habits. One that will obey me when I speak to him. In short, a good dog," said the wizard.

"Such a dog is hard to find," returned the glass-blower, who was busy making a blue glass flower pot with a pink glass rosebush in it, having green glass leaves and yellow glass roses.

The wizard watched him thoughtfully.

"Why cannot you blow me a dog out of glass?" he asked, presently.

"I can," declared the glass-blower; "but it would not bark at people, you know."

"Oh, I'll fix that easily enough," replied the other. "If I could not make a glass dog bark I would be a mighty poor wizard."

"Very well; if you can use a glass dog I'll be pleased to blow one for you. Only, you must pay for my work."

"Certainly," agreed the wizard. "But I have none of that horrid stuff you call money. You must take some of my wares in exchange."

The glass-blower considered the matter for a moment.

"Could you give me something to cure my rheumatism?" he asked.

"Oh, yes; easily."

"Then it's a bargain. I'll start the dog at once. What color of glass shall I use?"

"Pink is a pretty color," said the wizard, "and it's unusual for a dog, isn't it?"

"Very," answered the glass-blower; "but it shall be pink."

So the wizard went back to his studies and the glass-blower began to make the dog.

Next morning he entered the wizard's room with the glass dog under his arm and set it carefully upon the table. It was a beautiful pink in color, with a fine coat of spun glass, and about its neck was twisted a blue glass ribbon. Its eyes were specks of black glass and sparkled intelligently, as do many of the glass eyes worn by men.

The wizard expressed himself pleased with the glass-blower's skill and at once handed him a small vial.

"This will cure your rheumatism," he said.

"But the vial is empty!" protested the glass-blower.

"Oh, no; there is one drop of liquid in it," was the wizard's reply.

"Will one drop cure my rheumatism?" inquired the glass-blower, in wonder.

"Most certainly. That is a marvelous remedy. The one drop contained in the vial will cure instantly any kind of disease ever known to humanity. Therefore it is especially good for rheumatism. But guard it well, for it is the only drop of its kind in the world, and I've forgotten the recipe."

"Thank you," said the glass-blower, and went back to his room.

1 | **What did the wizard spend most of his time doing?**

    A. Answering the door as people kept knocking on his door

    B. Finding a dog that was good

    C. Scientific inventions

    D. Thoughtful studies

2 | **How good a wizard was he?**

    A. The one who knew all wizardry there is to know about

    B. An average wizard who had collected all the books of wizardry

    C. A studious wizard who spent his time finding a dog

    D. An angry wizard who hated people knocking on his door

3 | **What used to make the wizard not completely happy at his own house?**

    A. He could not find a good dog

    B. The neighbour always caused grief

    C. People kept disturbing him by knocking on his door

    D. He kept losing his valuable books of wizardry

4 | **How did the wizard plan to resolve the issue causing him to be unhappy?**

    A. By asking the glass-blower to stop making so much noise

    B. By stopping his search for a good dog

    C. By putting up a board asking people not to knock on the door

    D. By getting a dog that will keep people away from his door

5 **Which of the following best describes the dog that the wizard wanted?**

A. A glass dog

B. A pink dog

C. A good, clean dog that kept people away and that needed no feeding

D. A puppet dog that looked real

6 **What did the wizard ask the glass-blower to do?**

A. To blow him a glass dog

B. To stop making so much noise

C. To stop making blue glass flower pots

D. To answer the door when someone knocked

7 **What did the glass-blower want in return?**

A. Money

B. Fix for his broken limb

C. Cure for rheumatism

D. A magic pill

8 **Why could not the wizard pay the glass-blower any money?**

A. He had no money

B. He was a miser

C. He did not want to part with his hard earned money

D. He believed in saving and not spending

9 | **What did the wizard give in return for the pink glass dog?**

    A. Money

    B. Fix for his broken limb

    C. An empty vial

    D. A vial with a single drop of cure for any disease

10 | **Why was the content of the vial so vital?**

    A. Because it could cure any disease in the world

    B. Because there was only one drop of the cure left in the vial

    C. Because the wizard had forgotten the recipe for the cure

    D. All of the above

ANSWER SHEET

	A	B	C	D			A	B	C	D
1	⬒	⬒	⬒	⬒		6	⬒	⬒	⬒	⬒
2	⬒	⬒	⬒	⬒		7	⬒	⬒	⬒	⬒
3	⬒	⬒	⬒	⬒		8	⬒	⬒	⬒	⬒
4	⬒	⬒	⬒	⬒		9	⬒	⬒	⬒	⬒
5	⬒	⬒	⬒	⬒		10	⬒	⬒	⬒	⬒

EXERCISE 13

Instructions: Read the passage carefully and then answer the questions that follow. Record your answer on the answer sheet by choosing one of the options.

Mamma had gone down-town to shop. She had asked Nora to look after Jane Gladys, and Nora promised she would. But it was her afternoon for polishing the silver, so she stayed in the pantry and left Jane Gladys to amuse herself alone in the big sitting-room upstairs.

The little girl did not mind being alone, for she was working on her first piece of embroidery—a sofa pillow for papa's birthday present. So she crept into the big bay window and curled herself up on the broad sill while she bent her brown head over her work.

Soon the door opened and closed again, quietly. Jane Gladys thought it was Nora, so she didn't look up until she had taken a couple more stitches on a forget-me-not. Then she raised her eyes and was astonished to find a strange man in the middle of the room, who regarded her earnestly.

He was short and fat, and seemed to be breathing heavily from his climb up the stairs. He held a work silk hat in one hand and underneath his other elbow was tucked a good-sized book. He was dressed in a black suit that looked old and rather shabby, and his head was bald upon the top.

"Excuse me," he said, while the child gazed at him in solemn surprise. "Are you Jane Gladys Brown?"

"Yes, sir," she answered.

"Very good; very good, indeed!" he remarked, with a queer sort of smile. "I've had quite a hunt to find you, but I've succeeded at last."

"How did you get in?" inquired Jane Gladys, with a growing distrust of her visitor.

"That is a secret," he said, mysteriously.

This was enough to put the girl on her guard. She looked at the man and the man looked at her, and both looks were grave and somewhat anxious.

"What do you want?" she asked, straightening herself up with a dignified air.

"Ah!—now we are coming to business," said the man, briskly. "I'm going to be quite frank with you. To begin with, your father has abused me in a most ungentlemanly manner."

Jane Gladys got off the window sill and pointed her small finger at the door.

"Leave this room 'meejitly!" she cried, her voice trembling with indignation. "My papa is the best man in the world. He never 'bused anybody!"

"Allow me to explain, please," said the visitor, without paying any attention to her request to go away. "Your father may be very kind to you, for you are his little girl, you know. But when he's down-town in his office he's inclined to be rather severe, especially on book agents. Now, I called on him the other day and asked him to buy the 'Complete Works of Peter Smith,' and what do you suppose he did?"

She said nothing.

"Why," continued the man, with growing excitement, "he ordered me from his office, and had me put out of the building by the janitor! What do you think of such treatment as that from the 'best papa in the world,' eh?"

"I think he was quite right," said Jane Gladys.

"Oh, you do? Well," said the man, "I resolved to be revenged for the insult. So, as your father is big and strong and a dangerous man, I have decided to be revenged upon his little girl."

Jane Gladys shivered.

"What are you going to do?" she asked.

"I'm going to present you with this book," he answered, taking it from under his arm. Then he sat down on the edge of a chair, placed his hat on the rug and drew a fountain pen from his vest pocket.

"I'll write your name in it," said he. "How do you spell Gladys?"

"G-l-a-d-y-s," she replied.

"Thank you. Now this," he continued, rising and handing her the book with a bow, "is my revenge for your father's treatment of me. Perhaps he'll be sorry he didn't buy the 'Complete Works of Peter Smith.' Good-by, my dear."

He walked to the door, gave her another bow, and left the room, and Jane Gladys could see that he was laughing to himself as if very much amused.

When the door had closed behind the queer little man the child sat down in the window again and glanced at the book. It had a red and yellow cover and the word "Thingamajigs" was across the front in big letters.

Then she opened it, curiously, and saw her name written in black letters upon the first white leaf.

"He was a funny little man," she said to herself, thoughtfully.

She turned the next leaf, and saw a big picture of a clown, dressed in green and red and yellow, and having a very white face with three-cornered spots of red on each cheek and over the eyes. While she looked at this the book trembled in her hands, the leaf crackled and creaked and suddenly the clown jumped out of it and stood upon the floor beside her, becoming instantly as big as any ordinary clown.

QUESTIONS

| 1 | What was Nora busy doing in the pantry? |

A. Babysitting Jane

B. Working on her first piece of embroidery

C. Reading her favourite book

D. Polishing the silver

| 2 | What was the little girl Jane working on? |

A. Embroidering a sofa pill as a birthday gift for her dad

B. Polishing the silver with Nora

C. Playing on the window sill

D. Amusing herself upstairs

3	Which of the following best describes the stranger who appeared in Jane's room?

A. A tall, handsome man dressed in a black suit

(B.) A short, fat man dressed in an old shabby black suit

C. A short, fat man with a magicians hat

D. A short man that looked more a goblin than a man

4	Who was it that the stranger came looking for?

A. Nora

B. Jane's father

(C.) Jane

D. Mamma

5	Why did Jane ask the man to leave at once?

A. Because he did not tell her how he got into her room

(B.) Because he was a stranger and she did not want to talk to strangers

C. Because he was a mess in his old, shabby black suit

D. Because he said not so nice things about her father

6	What did the man want from Jane's father?

A. A book titled "Complete Works of Jane Smith"

B. A new suit

C. A book titled "Thingamajigs"

D. A book titled "Complete Works of Peter Smith"

7   **What was the reason for the man to come looking for Jane?**

    A.   To seek revenge

    B.   To present her a book

    C.   To steal from her the book he wanted her father to buy him

    D.   To learn how to spell "Gladys"

8   **What did the man give Jane?**

    A.   A book titled "Thingamajigs"

    B.   A book titled "Complete Works of Peter Smith"

    C.   A book titled "Complete Works of Jane Smith"

    D.   A book titled "G-l-a-d-y-s"

9   **Why do you think he had a smile on his face when he left the house?**

    A.   Because he had decided to forgive and not seek revenge any more

    B.   Because he thought little Jane was funny

    C.   Because he had gotten rid of his heavy book

    D.   Because he knew the book he gave Jane was no ordinary book and will help him exact his revenge

10   **Why did Jane think the man was funny?**

    A.   Because he said he wanted to seek revenge but instead left after gifting her a book

    B.   Because he did not know how to spell "Gladys"

    C.   Because he said funny things about her father

    D.   Because he looked like a clown from the book

ANSWER SHEET

1	A ☐	B ☐	C ☐	D ☐		6	A ☐	B ☐	C ☐	D ☐
2	A ☐	B ☐	C ☐	D ☐		7	A ☐	B ☐	C ☐	D ☐
3	A ☐	B ☐	C ☐	D ☐		8	A ☐	B ☐	C ☐	D ☐
4	A ☐	B ☐	C ☐	D ☐		9	A ☐	B ☐	C ☐	D ☐
5	A ☐	B ☐	C ☐	D ☐		10	A ☐	B ☐	C ☐	D ☐

EXERCISE 14

Instructions: Read the passage carefully and then answer the questions that follow. Record your answer on the answer sheet by choosing one of the options.

Jim was the son of a cowboy, and lived on the broad plains of Arizona. His father had trained him to lasso a bronco or a young bull with perfect accuracy, and had Jim possessed the strength to back up his skill he would have been as good a cowboy as any in all Arizona.

When he was twelve years old he made his first visit to the east, where Uncle Charles, his father's brother, lived. Of course Jim took his lasso with him, for he was proud of his skill in casting it, and wanted to show his cousins what a cowboy could do.

At first the city boys and girls were much interested in watching Jim lasso posts and fence pickets, but they soon tired of it, and even Jim decided it was not the right sort of sport for cities.

But one day the butcher asked Jim to ride one of his horses into the country, to a pasture that had been engaged, and Jim eagerly consented. He had been longing for a horseback ride, and to make it seem like old times he took his lasso with him.

He rode through the streets demurely enough, but on reaching the open country roads his spirits broke forth into wild jubilation, and, urging the butcher's horse to full gallop, he dashed away in true cowboy fashion.

Then he wanted still more liberty, and letting down the bars that led into a big field he began riding over the meadow and throwing his lasso at imaginary cattle, while he yelled and whooped to his heart's content.

Suddenly, on making a long cast with his lasso, the loop caught upon something and rested about three feet from the ground, while the rope drew taut and nearly pulled Jim from his horse.

This was unexpected. More than that, it was wonderful; for the field seemed bare of even a stump. Jim's eyes grew big with amazement, but he knew he had caught something when a voice cried out:

"Here, let go! Let go, I say! Can't you see what you've done?"

No, Jim couldn't see, nor did he intend to let go until he found out what was holding the loop of the lasso. So he resorted to an old trick his father had taught him and, putting the butcher's horse to a run, began riding in a circle around the spot where his lasso had caught.

As he thus drew nearer and nearer his quarry he saw the rope coil up, yet it looked to be coiling over nothing but air. One end of the lasso was made fast to a ring in the saddle, and when the rope was almost wound up and the horse began to pull away and snort with fear, Jim dismounted. Holding the reins of the bridle in one hand, he followed the rope, and an instant later saw an old man caught fast in the coils of the lasso.

His head was bald and uncovered, but long white whiskers grew down to his waist. About his body was thrown a loose robe of fine white linen. In one hand he bore a great scythe, and beneath the other arm he carried an hourglass.

While Jim gazed wonderingly upon him, this venerable old man spoke in an angry voice:

"Now, then—get that rope off as fast as you can! You've brought everything on earth to a standstill by your foolishness! Well—what are you staring at? Don't you know who I am?"

"No," said Jim, stupidly.

"Well, I'm Time—Father Time! Now, make haste and set me free—if you want the world to run properly."

"How did I happen to catch you?" asked Jim, without making a move to release his captive.

"I don't know. I've never been caught before," growled Father Time. "But I suppose it was because you were foolishly throwing your lasso at nothing."

"I didn't see you," said Jim.

"Of course you didn't. I'm invisible to the eyes of human beings unless they get within three feet of me, and I take care to keep more than that distance away from them. That's why I was crossing this field, where I supposed no one would be. And I should have been perfectly safe had it not been for your beastly lasso. Now, then," he added, crossly, "are you going to get that rope off?"

"Why should I?" asked Jim.

"Because everything in the world stopped moving the moment you caught me. I don't suppose you want to make an end of all business and pleasure, and war and love, and misery and ambition and everything else, do you? Not a watch has ticked since you tied me up here like a mummy!"

Jim laughed. It really was funny to see the old man wound round and round with coils of rope from his knees up to his chin.

"It'll do you good to rest," said the boy. "From all I've heard you lead a rather busy life."

"Indeed I do," replied Father Time, with a sigh. "I'm due in Kamchatka this very minute. And to think one small boy is upsetting all my regular habits!"

Mastering 11+ / COMPREHENSION / Practice Book ONE

"Too bad!" said Jim, with a grin. "But since the world has stopped anyhow, it won't matter if it takes a little longer recess. As soon as I let you go Time will fly again. Where are your wings?"

"I haven't any," answered the old man. "That is a story cooked up by someone who never saw me. As a matter of fact, I move rather slowly."

"I see, you take your time," remarked the boy. "What do you use that scythe for?"

"To mow down the people," said the ancient one. "Every time I swing my scythe some one dies."

"Then I ought to win a life-saving medal by keeping you tied up," said Jim. "Some folks will live this much longer."

"But they won't know it," said Father Time, with a sad smile; "so it will do them no good. You may as well untie me at once."

QUESTIONS

1   **Why did Jim take his lasso with him to the city?**

     A. Because he wanted to show-off his skills with the lasso

     B. Because he wanted to catch something useful

     C. Because he wanted to lasso posts and fence pickets

     D. Because he wanted to train his Uncle Charles

2   **Why was Jim quick to agree to the butcher's request to ride one of the horses into the country?**

     A. He was dying for a horse ride

     B. He had enough of the city

     C. He wanted to practise using lasso

     D. He was bored of his friends in the city

3 | **What did Jim catch with his lasso while riding through the country?**

    A. A young bull

    B. A bronco

    C. An invisible ancient being

    D. Time Machine

4 | **What do you think is a lasso?**

    A. A long stick with a sharp knife at the end of it

    B. A rope with a noose

    C. A rope to tie up a young bull or a bronco

    D. A scythe

5 | **Why couldn't Jim see what he had caught with his lasso until he got very close to it?**

    A. Because it was a day of dense fog

    B. Because it was a dusty affair

    C. Because no one could see Father Time unless they are within three feet from him

    D. Because Father Time had magical power of being invisible to human beings

6 | **What did the old man have under his arm?**

    A. A scythe

    B. A wrist watch

    C. A scroll

    D. An hourglass

7   **Everything in the world had come to a halt. Why?**

     A.   Because Father Time was resting

     B.   Because Father Time was caught by Jim

     C.   Because nature's hourglass had broken

     D.   Because of a curse that Jim accidentally invoked

8   **What according to Jim would be a good thing for Father Time?**

     A.   Stopping the use of the scythe

     B.   Start moving a bit faster

     C.   Show him his wings

     D.   Resting for a while

9   **What did the ancient one use his scythe for?**

     A.   To mow down people

     B.   To mow down lawn

     C.   To prune the bush

     D.   To cut the branches of a tree

10   **Why would locking up Father Time not save anyone's life?**

     A.   Because with Father Time tied up, the world is standstill

     B.   Because there are more than one Father Time

     C.   Because Father Time has nothing to do with people's life

     D.   Because Father Time had assistants who would continue doing the job for him

1	A	B	C	D		6	A	B	C	D
2	A	B	C	D		7	A	B	C	D
3	A	B	C	D		8	A	B	C	D
4	A	B	C	D		9	A	B	C	D
5	A	B	C	D		10	A	B	C	D

Instructions: Read the passage carefully and then answer the questions that follow. Record your answer on the answer sheet by choosing one of the options.

Not many years ago there lived on a stony, barren New England farm a man and his wife. They were sober, honest people, working hard from early morning until dark to enable them to secure a scanty living from their poor land.

Their house, a small, one-storied building, stood upon the side of a steep hill, and the stones lay so thickly about it that scarce anything green could grow from the ground. At the foot of the hill, a quarter of a mile from the house by the winding path, was a small brook, and the woman was obliged to go there for water and to carry it up the hill to the house. This was a tedious task, and with the other hard work that fell to her share had made her gaunt and bent and lean.

Yet she never complained, but meekly and faithfully performed her duties, doing the housework, carrying the water and helping her husband hoe the scanty crop that grew upon the best part of their land.

One day, as she walked down the path to the brook, her big shoes scattering the pebbles right and left, she noticed a large beetle lying upon its back and struggling hard with its little legs to turn over, that its feet might again touch the ground. But this it could not accomplish; so the woman, who had a kind heart, reached down and gently turned the beetle with her finger. At once it scampered from the path and she went on to the brook.

The next day, as she came for water, she was surprised to see the beetle again lying upon its back and struggling helplessly to turn. Once more the woman stopped and set him upon his feet; and then, as she stooped over the tiny creature, she heard a small voice say:

"Oh, thank you! Thank you so much for saving me!"

Half frightened at hearing a beetle speak in her own language, the woman started back and exclaimed:

"La sakes! Surely you can't talk like humans!" Then, recovering from her alarm, she again bent over the beetle, who answered her:

"Why shouldn't I talk, if I have anything to say?

"'Cause you're a bug," replied the woman.

"That is true; and you saved my life—saved me from my enemies, the sparrows. And this is the second time you have come to my assistance, so I owe you a debt of gratitude. Bugs value their lives as much as human beings, and I am a more important creature than you, in your ignorance, may suppose. But, tell me, why do you come each day to the brook?"

"For water," she answered, staring stupidly down at the talking beetle.

"Isn't it hard work?" the creature inquired.

"Yes; but there's no water on the hill," said she.

"Then dig a well and put a pump in it," replied the beetle.

She shook her head.

"My man tried it once; but there was no water," she said, sadly.

"Try it again," commanded the beetle; "and in return for your kindness to me I will make this promise: if you do not get water from the well you will get that which is more precious to you. I must go now. Do not forget. Dig a well."

And then, without pausing to say good-by, it ran swiftly away and was lost among the stones.

The woman returned to the house much perplexed by what the beetle had said, and when her husband came in from his work she told him the whole story.

The poor man thought deeply for a time, and then declared:

"Wife, there may be truth in what the bug told you. There must be magic in the world yet, if a beetle can speak; and if there is such a thing as magic we may get water from the well. The pump I bought to use in the well which proved to be dry is now lying in the barn, and the only expense in following the talking bug's advice will be the labor of digging the hole. Labor I am used to; so I will dig the well."

Next day he set about it, and dug so far down in the ground that he could hardly reach the top to climb out again; but not a drop of water was found.

So the following day he made a long ladder, which he put into the hole; and then he dug, and dug, and dug, until the top of the ladder barely reached the top of the hole. But still there was no water.

When the woman next went to the brook with her pail she saw the beetle sitting upon a stone beside her path. So she stopped and said:

"My husband has dug the well; but there is no water."

"Do as I commanded; put in the pump, and if you do not get water I promise you something still more precious." Saying which, the beetle swiftly slid from the stone and disappeared. The woman went back to the house and told her husband what the bug had said.

"Well," replied the simple fellow, "there can be no harm in trying."

So he got the pump from the barn and placed it in the well, and then he took hold of the handle and began to pump, while his wife stood by to watch what would happen.

No water came, but after a few moments a gold piece dropped from the spout of the pump, and then another, and another, until several handfuls of gold lay in a little heap upon the ground.

The man stopped pumping then and ran to help his wife gather the gold pieces into her apron; but their hands trembled so greatly through excitement and joy that they could scarcely pick up the sparkling coins.

Suddenly the woman spoke.

"Husband, the beetle said truly when he declared we should get something more precious than water from the well. But run at once and take away the handle from the pump, lest anyone should pass this way and discover our secret."

So the man ran to the pump and removed the handle, which he carried to the house and hid underneath the bed.

QUESTIONS

1 **What does the word "sober" mean in the context of describing the honest and hardworking family in this passage?**

    A. Moderate

    B. Playful

    C. Frivolous

    D. Greedy

2 | **What had made the woman gaunt, bent and lean?**

    A. Carrying of water from the brook every day

    B. The hard work that fell to her share

    C. Helping her husband weed the crop

    D. All of the above

3 | **Which of the following best describes the woman in this story?**

    A. A hardworking, honest and kind woman

    B. A hardworking, innocent but weak woman

    C. A weak, lean woman who had not much intelligence

    D. A greedy woman who wants all the riches for herself

4 | **Who are the enemies of the beetle?**

    A. The woman and her husband

    B. The pebbles that spattered on the beetle

    C. The pigeons

    D. The sparrows

5 | **Why did the beetle owe the woman a debt of gratitude?**

    A. Because she saved its life once from the sparrows

    B. Because she was kind and stooped over the beetle instead of stepping on it

    C. Because she saved its life twice by turning it over when the beetle was struggling on its back

    D. Because she was kind enough to have a conversation with a beetle

6 | **What did the beetle ask the woman to do?**

    A. To dig a well and put a pump in it

    B. To stop fetching water from the brook

    C. To stop doing the hard work

    D. To make a promise never to help another beetle

7 | **What was the reaction of the woman's husband when he heard of the promise made by the beetle?**

    A. He laughed and ignored her

    B. He thought she must have been day dreaming

    C. He thought there might be some truth and decided to try digging a well

    D. He decided to go find the beetle himself to confirm the promise

8 | **What did the couple get from the pump?**

    A. Gold coins

    B. Water

    C. Beetles

    D. Handful of pebbles

9 | **Do you think the beetle kept the promise made to the woman?**

    A. Yes, as the pump gave them the water

    B. No, the pump did not give them the water; hence the woman will have to continue the hard work of fetching water from the brook

    C. Yes, as the pump gave the something better than water

    D. No, as the gold coins are no good to the honest and hardworking couple

10	Why did the man hide the handle of the pump?

A. Because the woman did not want anyone else to know their secret

B. Because they had pumped enough gold coins

C. Because they did not get water from the pump

D. Because there was no truth in what the beetle had said

ANSWER SHEET

	A	B	C	D			A	B	C	D
1	A ⊏⊐	B ⊏⊐	C ⊏⊐	D ⊏⊐		6	A ⊏⊐	B ⊏⊐	C ⊏⊐	D ⊏⊐
2	A ⊏⊐	B ⊏⊐	C ⊏⊐	D ⊏⊐		7	A ⊏⊐	B ⊏⊐	C ⊏⊐	D ⊏⊐
3	A ⊏⊐	B ⊏⊐	C ⊏⊐	D ⊏⊐		8	A ⊏⊐	B ⊏⊐	C ⊏⊐	D ⊏⊐
4	A ⊏⊐	B ⊏⊐	C ⊏⊐	D ⊏⊐		9	A ⊏⊐	B ⊏⊐	C ⊏⊐	D ⊏⊐
5	A ⊏⊐	B ⊏⊐	C ⊏⊐	D ⊏⊐		10	A ⊏⊐	B ⊏⊐	C ⊏⊐	D ⊏⊐

ANSWERS

Check www.mastering11plus.com/answers
for updated answers for this book.

ANSWERS:

EXERCISE 1		EXERCISE 2		EXERCISE 3		EXERCISE 4		EXERCISE 5	
1	C	1	D	1	A	1	B	1	A
2	C	2	C	2	B	2	B	2	B
3	B	3	A	3	C	3	A	3	A
4	D	4	C	4	D	4	B	4	A
5	B	5	A	5	C	5	B	5	D
6	C	6	A	6	A	6	C	6	D
7	A	7	C	7	B	7	A	7	C
8	D	8	C	8	B	8	C	8	A
9	B	9	A	9	C	9	B	9	B
10	A	10	D	10	A	10	A	10	B

Mastering 11+ / COMPREHENSION / Practice Book ONE

ANSWERS:

EXERCISE 6		EXERCISE 7		EXERCISE 8		EXERCISE 9		EXERCISE 10	
1	C	1	D	1	D	1	A	1	A
2	A	2	C	2	C	2	A	2	D
3	B	3	A	3	C	3	A	3	A
4	A	4	D	4	B	4	B	4	C
5	B	5	A	5	C	5	D	5	B
6	A	6	C	6	C	6	C	6	D
7	C	7	A	7	A	7	A	7	B
8	B	8	B	8	B	8	A	8	A
9	A	9	B	9	B	9	C	9	D
10	A	10	C	10	B	10	B	10	C

ANSWERS:

EXERCISE 11		EXERCISE 12		EXERCISE 13		EXERCISE 14		EXERCISE 15	
1	D	1	D	1	D	1	A	1	A
2	A	2	A	2	A	2	A	2	D
3	D	3	C	3	B	3	C	3	A
4	A	4	D	4	C	4	B	4	D
5	A	5	C	5	D	5	C	5	C
6	A	6	A	6	D	6	D	6	A
7	A	7	C	7	A	7	B	7	C
8	C	8	A	8	A	8	D	8	A
9	A	9	D	9	D	9	A	9	C
10	D	10	D	10	A	10	A	10	A

Other books in the Mastering 11+ series:

- ➢ English & Verbal Reasoning – Practice Book 1
- ➢ English & Verbal Reasoning – Practice Book 2
- ➢ English & Verbal Reasoning – Practice Book 3

- ➢ Cloze Tests – Practice Book 1
- ➢ Cloze Tests – Practice Book 2
- ➢ Cloze Tests – Practice Book 3

- ➢ Maths / Numerical Reasoning – Practice Book 1
- ➢ Maths / Numerical Reasoning – Practice Book 2
- ➢ Maths / Numerical Reasoning – Practice Book 3

- ➢ Comprehension – Multiple Choice Exercise Book 2
- ➢ Comprehension – Multiple Choice Exercise Book 3

- ➢ CEM Practice Papers – Pack 1
- ➢ CEM Practice Papers – Pack 2
- ➢ CEM Practice Papers – Pack 3
- ➢ CEM Practice Papers – Pack 4

All queries via email to enquiry@mastering11plus.com

Mastering11plus.com © 2014, ashkraft educational